Compiled by EMMA WOOD

© Printforce Limited, 2002

British Library Cataloguing in Publication Data
A CIP catalogue record for this book is available from the British Library

ISBN 0 948834 18 8

Printed in Great Britain

CONTENTS

Kids' Songtime!

INTRODUCTION

This selection of songs is aimed at those working with children aged from 5-14. It has been compiled largely by word-of-mouth so we are not always sure where the songs originated.

We have given an idea of the tune for each song – we are sorry but to locate and print the full music would be virtually impossible! Experience has shown us that many people hear songs at camp fires and other gatherings and find it easy to remember the tunes but not the words. This compendium will help you find those elusive words. Sheet music for some of the songs in this book may be obtained from music publishers and some appear in religious song books.

For those of you looking for songs more suited to those over 14, we recommend the Printforce books *Campfire Songs* and *Campfire Songs 2*.

We hope you enjoy these songs and that they will give you the chance to add a little sparkle to your family or youth group's activities!

Emma Wood – January 2002

My thanks to Timothy, Oliver, Joshua and Daniel for putting up with my research and trying out the songs with me.

ACKNOWLEDGEMENT: The songs in this book have come from a variety of sources, primarily word of mouth. We apologise if we have not given appropriate credit.

Down the air

(Tune: traditional)

Down the air,
Everywhere,
God is sending rain.
Dropping, dropping,
Dropping, dropping,
Down the window pane.
Pitter, patter,
Pitter, patter,
Down the window pane.
Pitter, patter,
Pitter, patter,
Thank God for the rain.

Twinkle, twinkle little star

(Tune: traditional)

Twinkle, twinkle little star,
How I wonder what you are,
Up above the world so high,
Like a diamond in the sky.
Twinkle, twinkle little star
How I wonder what you are.

Kids' Songtime!

Alice the camel
(Tune: traditional camp fire)

Alice the camel had three humps,
Alice the camel had three humps,
Alice the camel had three humps,
So, go, Alice GO! Bum, bum, bum.

Alice the camel had two humps,
Alice the camel had two humps,
Alice the camel had two humps,
So, go, Alice GO! Bum, bum, bum.

Alice the camel had one hump,
Alice the camel had one hump,
Alice the camel had one hump,
So, go, Alice GO! Bum, bum, bum.

Alice the camel had no humps,
Alice the camel had no humps,
Alice the camel had no humps,
So Alice was a mule!

Actions:
Bend knees when word 'humps' is sung,
wiggle bottoms from side to side when
the phrase 'Bum bum bum' is sung.

A great big happy smile
(Tune: John Brown's Body)

I've something in my pocket that belongs across my
    face,
I keep it close beside me in a most convenient place,
You'll never ever guess it, though you'd try for quite a
    while,
So I'll take it out and put it on, it's a great big happy
    smile.

B.I.N.G.O.
(Tune: traditional)

There was a man who had a dog,
And Bingo was his name,
B-I-N-G-O, B-I-N-G-O, B-I-N-G-O,
And Bingo was his name.

*(Repeat five times. The second time around, replace
the 'O' with a hand clap. The third time, replace the
'G' & 'O' with a handclap... and so on.)*

My hat it has three corners
(Tune: traditional/chanted)

My hat it has three corners
Three corners has my hat
And had it not three corners
It would not be my hat.

Brush your teeth

(Tune: Row, row, row your boat)

Brush, brush, brush your teeth,
Morning noon and night,
See your dentist twice a year,
And you'll be alright.

In my father's house

(Tune: traditional)

Oh come and go with me *(allelujah),*
To my father's house.
To my father's house,
To my father's house,
Oh come and go with me *(allelujah)*
To my father's house
Where there's peace *(forever)* peace *(forever)* peace.

There's sweet communion there, *(allelujah),*
In my father's house.
In my father's house.
In my father's house.
There's sweet communion there, *(allelujah),*
In my father's house.
Where there's peace *(forever)* peace *(forever)* peace.

Head and shoulders

(Tune: There's a tavern in the town)

Head, shoulders, knees and toes, knees and toes.
Head, shoulders, knees and toes, knees and toes.
And eyes and ears and mouth and nose,
Head, shoulders, knees and toes, knees and toes.

(Actions: Using both hands, point to the parts of the body as they are spoken. Great fun can be had by repeating the song and being quiet when the word 'Head' is meant to be sung. The next time it is repeated, miss out 'Head' and 'Shoulders', whilst still doing the actions... and so on.)

The Grand Old Duke of York

Oh, the grand old Duke of York,
He had ten thousand men,
He marched them up to the top of the hill,
And he marched them down again.
And when they were up they were up,
And when they were down they were down,
And when they were only half way up,
They were neither up nor down.

(Actions: Participants should be standing and, whenever the word 'Up' is said, they sit down, and when 'Down' is said, they stand up.)

Kids' Songtime!

Music man

(Tune: traditional)

I am the music man and I come from down your way
And I can play... *(What can you play?)*
I play the piano.
Oh, pia-pia-piano, piano, piano
Pia-pia-piano, pia-piano.

I am the music man and I come from down your way
And I can play... *(What can you play?)*
I play the the big bass drum.

Oh, boom, boom, boom, boom, boom, boom, boom,
Boom, boom, boom, boom, boom, boom.
Boom, boom, boom, boom, boom, boom, boom.
Boom, boom, boom, boom, boom.

Verse 3: Triangle – ting-a-ling-a-ling

Verse 4: Bagpipes – Na-na-na.

Verse 5: Trombone – Um-pa, um-pa, um-pa.

Verse 6: Viola – Vio-vio-viola.

Baby bumble bee

(Tune: traditional)

I'm taking home a baby bumble bee,
   Actions: Cup hands to take bee home.
Won't my mummy be surprised at me,
I'm taking home a baby bumble bee,
Ow! Ow! It stung me!

So I'm squashing up a baby bumble bee,
   Actions: Squash hands together
Won't my mummy be surprised at me,
I'm squashing up a baby bumble bee,
Errr! There's blood on me!

So, I'm licking up a baby bumble bee,
   Actions: Lick hands.
Won't my mummy be surprised at me,
I'm licking up a baby bumble bee,
But errr! There's no salt!

So I'm bringing up a baby bumble bee,
   Actions: Cup hands.
Won't my mummy be surpised at me,
I'm bringing up a baby bumble bee,
But errr! All over me!

I'm washing off the baby bumble bee,
   Actions: Pretend to wash hands.
Won't my mummy be surprised at me,
I'm washing off a baby bumble bee,
Hey mum, What's for tea?

Everywhere we go

(Tune: traditional - sung as a yell, with one group or a leader singing one phrase and the other group repeating it as an echo)

Everywhere we go (everywhere we go),
People always ask us (people always ask us),
Who we are (who we are),
Where we come from (where we come from),
So we tell them (so we tell them),
We're from 'London' *(say your own place)*
    (we're from London),
Mighty, mighty London (mighty, mighty London),
And if they can't hear us (and if they can't hear us),
We shout a little louder! (we shout a little louder!)

(Keep repeating this until it gets very loud indeed and, on the last line of the final time, sing:And if they can't hear us... THEY MUST BE DEAF!)

Meatball
(Tune: On top of old Smokey)

On top of spaghetti, all covered with cheese,
I lost my poor meatball, when somebody sneezed.

It fell from the table and onto the floor,
And then my poor meatball rolled out of the door.

Out into the garden and under a bush,
And then my poor meatball was nothing but mush.

Three Blind Mice
(Tune: Three blind mice, albeit loosely!)

Three blind mice, three blind mice,
The same mice twice, the same mice twice,
Kindly note that there's only three,
And none of them was a bumble bee,
A kangaroo or a chimpanzee,
A hippopotamus or a flea,
No – they were only M-I-C-E,
And were as blind as blind could be,
In other words they could not see,
And that was the infirmity
Of three blind mice.

Cecil is a caterpillar

(Tune: Chant)

Cecil is a caterpillar, Cecil is my friend,
Last time I saw Cecil, he was this big…
I said to Cecil, 'What have you done?'
He said, 'I've eaten my mum.'

Cecil is a caterpillar, Cecil is my friend,
Last time I saw Cecil he was this big…
I said to Cecil, 'What have you done?'
He said, 'I've eaten my dad!'

Cecil is a caterpillar, Cecil is my friend,
Last time I saw Cecil, he was this big…
I said to Cecil, 'What have you done?'
He said, 'I've eaten my Grandma and Grandad.'

Cecil is a caterpillar, Cecil is my friend,
Last time I saw Cecil, he was this big…
I said to Cecil, 'What have you done?'
He said, 'I've been sick!'

I'm a little teapot

(Tune: traditional)

I'm a little teapot, short and stout,
Here's my handle, here's my spout,
When I see the tea cups hear me shout:
"Tip me up and pour me out!"

Five little speckled frogs

(Tune: traditional)

Five little speckled frogs, sat on a speckled log,
Eating some most delicious bugs, yum yum!
One jumped into the pool, where it was nice and cool,
Then there were four green speckled frogs, glug, glug!

Four little speckled frogs, sat on a speckled log,
Eating some most delicious bugs, yum yum!
One jumped into the pool, where it was nice and cool,
Then there were three green speckled frogs, glug, glug!

Three little speckled frogs, sat on a speckled log,
Eating some most delicious bugs, yum yum!
One jumped into the pool, where it was nice and cool,
Then there were two green speckled frogs, glug, glug!

Two little speckled frogs, sat on a speckled log,
Eating some most delicious bugs, yum yum!
One jumped into the pool, where it was nice and cool,
Then there was one green speckled frog, glug, glug!

One little speckled frog, sat on a speckled log,
Eating some most delicious bugs, yum yum!
He jumped into the pool, where it was nice and cool,
Then there were no green speckled frogs, glug, glug!

Waltzing Matilda

(Tune: traditional)

Once a jolly swagman camped by a billabong,
Under the shade of a coolibah tree,
And he sang as he watched and waited till his billy
    boiled,
'You'll come a-waltzing Matilda with me.'

'Waltzing Matilda, waltzing Matilda,
You'll come a-waltzing Matilda with me,
And he sang as he watched and waited till his billy
    boiled,
You'll come a-waltzing Matilda with me'.

Have you ever seen a whale

(Tune: traditional)

Have you ever, ever, ever, ever, ever,
Have you ever, ever, ever seen a whale?
You must never, never, never, never, never,
You must never, never tread upon its tail.

For if you ever, ever, ever, ever, ever,
If you ever, ever, tread upon its tail
You will never, never, never, never, never,
You will never ever live to tell the tale.

Swatting skeeters
(Tune: I'm forever blowing bubbles)

I'm forever swatting skeeters,
Little beasts that buzz and bite,
They're always nigh, in earth and sky,
And like my dreams they come at night.
They are always hiding,
They are everywhere,
I'm forever swatting skeeters,
Little demons of the air.

Nellie
(Tune: 'Aunt Jemima')

Nellie ate some marmalade,
Nellie ate some jam,
Nellie ate some oysters,
And Nellie ate some ham.
Nellie ate some yummy cake,
And drank some ginger-beer,
And then Nellie wondered what made her feel so queer.

Oh! Up came the marmalade
And up came the jam,
Oh! Up came the oysters
And up came the ham,
Oh! Up came the yummy cake
Up came the ginger-beer,
And then Nellie knew what made her feel so queer.

My daddy had an apple

(Tune: 'Did you ever see a lassie')

1: My daddy had an apple, an apple, an apple,
   My daddy had an apple with a green worm inside.

Chorus:
A fuzzy one, a wuzzy one, a big fat (slurp) juicy one.
My daddy had an apple with a green worm inside.

He went to see the doctor, the doctor, the doctor,
He went to see the doctor with a green worm inside.

2: He went into hospital, a hospital, a hospital
   He went into hospital, with a green worm inside.

3: He had an operation…

4: But the doctor couldn't find it…

5: Soon after that he died…

6: Then he went to heaven…

7: He stayed there ever after…

Found a peanut

(Tune: Darling Clementine)

Found a peanut, found a peanut,
Found a peanut just now,
Found a peanut, found a peanut,
Found a peanut just now.

Ate a peanut, ate a peanut,
Ate a peanut just now,
Ate a peanut, ate a peanut,
Ate a peanut, just now.

Got a tummy ache, got a tummy ache,
Got a tummy ache just now,
Got a tummy ache, got a tummy ache,
Got a tummy ache just now.

Called the doctor, called the doctor,
Called the doctor just now,
Called the doctor, called the doctor,
Called the doctor, just now.

Operation, operation,
Operation just now,
Operation, operation
Operation, just now.

Continued....

Kids' Songtime!

Died and went to heaven,
Went to heaven, went to heaven just now
Went to heaven, went to heaven
Went to heaven just now.

Found a peanut, found a peanut
Found a peanut, just now.
Found a peanut, found a peanut,
Found a peanut, just now.

If you're happy and you know it
(Tune: traditional)

If you're happy and you know it clap your hands,
> *(clap clap)*
If you're happy and you know it clap your hands,
> *(clap clap)*
If you're happy and you know it and you really want to
> show it,
If you're happy and you know it clap your hands
> *(clap clap)*

Repeat, doing the actions as appropriate:
> Stamp your feet
> Nod your head
> Turn around
> Shout 'we are'

Pizza Hut

(Tune: A Ram Sam Sam)

A Pizza Hut, a Pizza Hut,
Kentucky Fried Chicken and a Pizza Hut,
A Pizza Hut, a Pizza Hut,
Kentucky Fried Chicken and a Pizza Hut,
McDonald's, McDonald's
Kentucky Fried Chicken and a Pizza Hut,
McDonald's, McDonald's
Kentucky Fried Chicken and a Pizza Hut.

A Burger King, a Burger King
A greasy café and a Burger King
A Burger King, a Burger King
A greasy café and a Burger King
A Wimpy, a Wimpy,
A greasy café and a Burger King
A Wimpy, a Wimpy,
A greasy café and a Burger King.

A kebab shop, a kebab shop,
A take away and a kebab shop,
A kebab shop, a kebab shop,
A take away and a kebab shop,
A chippy, a chippy,
A take away and a kebab shop,
A chippy, a chippy,
A take away and a kebab shop,

continued...

Kids' Songtime!

A Little Chef, a Little Chef,
A Harvester and a Little Chef,
A Little Chef, a Little Chef,
A Harvester and a Little Chef,
A curry, a curry, a Harvester and a Little Chef,
A curry, a curry, a Harvester and a Little Chef,

The wee wee song
(Tune: traditional)

When I was a wee wee tot,
They took me from my wee wee cot,
They put me on my wee wee pot,
To see if I would wee or not.

When they found that I would not,
They took me from my wee wee pot,
They put me in my wee wee cot,
And there I wee wee'd quite a lot.

Three chocolate eclairs

(Tune: traditional)

Three chocolate eclairs, three chocolate eclairs,
Three chocolate eclairs, sitting on a plate,
Gobble, gobble, gobble.

Two chocolate eclairs, two chocolate eclairs,
Two chocolate eclairs, sitting on a plate,
Gobble, gobble, gobble.

One chocolate eclair, one chocolate eclair,
One chocolate eclair, sitting on a plate,
Gobble, gobble, gobble.

No chocolate eclairs, no chocolate eclairs,
No chocolate eclairs, sitting on a plate,
Bleurrgh!

One chocolate eclair, one chocolate eclair,
One chocolate eclair, sitting on a plate,
Bleurrgh!

Two chocolate eclairs, two chocolate eclairs,
Two chocolate eclairs, sitting on a plate,
Bleurrgh!

Three chocolate eclairs, three chocolate eclairs,
Three chocolate eclairs, sitting on a plate.

Kids' Songtime!

We are the red men
(Tune: traditional)

We are the red men tall and quaint,
In our feathers and war paint.

Pow wow, pow wow,
We're the men of the old dun cow,
All of us are red men,
Feathers in our head men,
Down amongst the dead men,
Ugh! Pow wow, pow wow.

The worm song
(Tune: traditional)

Nobody likes me, everybody hates me,
I think I'll go and eat worms,
Long worms, short worms, fat worms, thin worms,
Gooey, gooey, gooey, gooey worms.
Well you cut their heads off and suck out the juice,
And throw their skins away,
Nobody knows how I survive,
On worms three times a day.

The leapfrog song

(Tune: John Brown's body)

A busy buzzy bumble bee went busily buzzing by,
A busy buzzy bumble bee went busily buzzing by,
A busy buzzy bumble bee went busily buzzing by,
As the end of the day drew near.

Chorus:
They were only playing leapfrog
They were only playing leapfrog
They were only playing leapfrog
As the end of the day drew near.

One grasshopper hopped right over the other
    grasshopper's back…

One hedgehog edged up the hedge, the other
    hedgehog edged down….

One photographer photographed the other
    photographer's back…

One flea caught another flea, falling down on his
    back…

Kids' Songtime!

A Ram Sam Sam

(Tune: traditional)

A ram sam sam, A ram sam sam,
Gooli gooli gooli gooli gooli,
Ram sam sam.
A ram sam sam, A ram sam sam,
Gooli gooli gooli gooli gooli,
Ram sam sam.
A ra-vi, A ra-vi
Gooli gooli gooli gooli gooli,
Ram sam sam.
A ra-vi, A ra-vi
Gooli gooli gooli gooli gooli,
Ram sam sam.

Down by the station

(Tune: traditional)

Down by the station, early in the morning,
See the little puffer billies – all in a row,
See the engine driver turn a little handle
Chug! Chug! Whoo! Whoo! Off we go…

Gonna build a house

(Tune: traditional - 'Gilly gilly, osenfeather...')

Gonna build a house (gonna build a house),
With a chimney tall (with a chimney tall),
Gonna build a roof (gonna build a roof),
And a garden wall (and a garden wall),
And a big front door you can open wide,
Two small windows you can look inside,
Gonna build a house (Gonna build a house),
Gonna build a ho-u-se

Do your ears hang low?

(Tune: traditional)

Do your ears hang low,
Do they wobble to and fro,
Can you tie them in a knot,
Can you tie them in a bow?
Can you throw them over your shoulder
Like a Regimental soldier?
Do your ears hang low?

(Actions: simply do the actions suggested by the words!)

<u>She'll be coming round the mountain</u>

(Tune: traditional)

She'll be coming round the mountain when she comes,
She'll be coming round the mountain when she comes,
She'll be coming round the mountain,
Coming round the mountain,
Coming round the mountain when she comes

Chorus:
Singing "Eye-eye yippee, yippee-yi!
Singing "Eye-eye yippee, yippee-yi!
Singing "Eye-eye yippee,Eye-eye yippee,
Singing "Eye-eye yippee, yippee-yi!

She'll be driving six white horses... etc

We will all go out to meet her... etc

We will kill the old red rooster... etc

We will all have chicken and dumplings etc

Cottage in a wood
(Tune: traditional)

In a cottage in a wood,
Little old man at the window stood,
Saw a rabbit running by,
Frightened as could be.

'Help me, help me, sir,' she said,
'Ere the huntsman shoots me dead.'
'Come, little rabbit, come with me,
Happy we will be.'

Life is but a melancholy flower
(Tune: Frere Jacques - 4 part round)

Life is butter, life is butter
Melancholy flower, melancholy flower,
Life is but a melon, life is but a melon,
Cauliflower, cauliflower.

The Kookaburra
(Tune: traditional - 4 part round)

Kookaburra sits on an old gum tree,
Merry, merry king of the bush is he,
Laugh, kookaburra, laugh, kookaburra,
Gay your life must be.

Animal fair

(Tune: traditional - round)

I went to the animal fair,
The birds and the beasts were there
The blue baboon by the light of the moon
Was combing his auburn hair,
The monkey fell out of his bunk. *(clap)*
And slid down the elephant's trunk 'Wheee!'
The elephant sneezed and fell on his knees,
And what became of the monkey, monkey, monkey,
    monkey?

*(Repeat a second time with half of the singers chanting
'monkey, monkey, monkey'; the other half singing the
song. Then switch around!)*

God's love is like a circle

(Tune: traditional)

God's love is like a circle,
A circle big and round,
And when you have a circle,
No ending can be found,
And so the love of God,
Goes on eternally,
For ever and for ever,
I know that God loves me.

Working on the railroad

(Tune: traditional)

I've been working on the railroad,
All the live-long day,
I've been working on the railroad,
Just to pass the time away,
Can't you hear the whistle blowing?
Rise up so early in the morn,
Can't you hear the Captain calling?
'Dinah, blow your horn'.

Dinah, won't you blow,
Dinah, won't you blow,
Dinah, won't you blow your horn?
Dinah, won't you blow,
Dinah, won't you blow,
Dinah, won't you blow your horn?

Camp fire's burning

(Tune: London's burning)

Camp fire's burning, camp fire's burning,
Draw nearer, draw nearer,
In the glowing, in the glowing,
Come sing and be merry

Kids' Songtime!

We're all together again
(Tune: traditional)

We're all together again, we're here, we're here.
We're all together again, we're here, we're here.
And who knows when, we'll be all together again,
Singing we're all together again, we're here, we're here.

I know a song that'll get on your nerves
(Tune: traditional)

I know a song that'll get on your nerves,
Get on your nerves, get on your nerves,
I know a song that'll get on your nerves,
Get, get, get on your nerves.

(Repeat ad nauseum!)

Terrible collision
(Tune: traditional)

Terrible collision on the railway line,
Poor cow didn't see the red light shine,
Oh it happened long ago
And they're working on it now,
Sorting out the engine from the poor old cow, poor old
    cow.
*(Repeat a second time with half of the singers chanting
 'Poor old cow'; the other half singing the
song. Then switch around!)*

The bear went over the mountain
(Tune: For he's a jolly good fellow)

The bear went over the mountain
The bear went over the mountain
The bear went over the mountain
To see what he could see

And what do you think he saw?
And what do you think he saw?
The other side of the mountain.
The other side of the mountain.
The other side of the mountain.
Was all that he could see.

Boa-constrictor
(Tune: traditional)

Oh I'm being eaten by a Boa-constrictor,
A Boa-constrictor, a Boa-constrictor.
I'm being eaten by a Boa-constrictor,
And I don't like it one little bit.
Oh no, he's up to my toes.
Oh gee, he's up to my knees.
Oh fiddle, he's up to my middle.
Oh heck, he's up to my neck.
Oh dread, he's up to my GULP!

*(Actions: Touch the parts of your body with both hands
as you sing them.)*

Chick, Chick, Chick, Chick, Chicken
(Tune: traditional)

Chick, Chick, Chick, Chick, Chicken,
Lay a little egg for me.
Chick, Chick, Chick, Chick, Chicken,
I want one for my tea.
I haven't had an egg since breakfast,
And now it's half past three, so,
Chick, Chick, Chick, Chick, Chicken.
Lay a little egg for me.

(Repeat with half of the singers chanting a chicken's sound: Brarr, brar-brar; Brarr, brar-brar... etc, the other half singing the song. Then switch around!)

When the pig's a failure
(Tune: traditional - round)

When the pig's a failure,
He straightens out his tail,
But piggies tails are curly,
'Cos piggies never fail!

Funny old king
(Tune: traditional)

A funny old king with a big nose ring,
Fell in love with a dusky maid,
And every night in the pale moonlight,
Across the sea he waded.
He cuddled and kissed his pretty little miss,
In the shade of the bamboo tree,
And every night in the pale moonlight,
It sounded like this to me:
Tarumph (kiss kiss) tarumph (kiss kiss)
Tarumph taryaryay
Tarumph (kiss kiss) tarumph (kiss kiss)
Tarumph taryaryay.

Chew, chew
(Tune: Row, row, row your boat)

Chew, chew, chew your food,
Slowly through the meal,
The more you talk,
The less you'll eat,
The better you will feel.

The ants went marching

(Tune: traditional)

The ants went marching 1 by 1,
Hurrah, hurrah,
The ants went marching 1 by 1,
Hurrah, hurrah,
The ants went marching 1 by 1,
The little one stopped to suck his thumb,
And they all went marching down, to the earth,
To get out, of the rain, boom, boom, boom

The ants went marching 2 by 2
The little one stopped to tie his shoe

3 – climb a tree
4 – shut the door
5 – wave goodbye
6 – pick up sticks
7 – look to heaven
8 – shut the gate
9 – look at the time
10 – shout The End!

Did you ever see a Lassie
(Tune: traditional)

Did you ever see a lassie,
A lassie, a lassie,
Did you ever see a lassie,
Who acted like this?

And this way and that way,
And this way and that way,
Did you ever see a lassie,
Who acted like this?

Punchinello
(Tune: traditional)

Who comes here?
Punchinello, little fellow,
Who comes here?
Punchinello, little dear.

What can he do?
Punchinello, little fellow,
What can he do?
Punchinello little man.

We'll do it too,
Punchinello, little fellow
We'll do it too,
Punchinello, little man.

Kids' Songtime!

Rock my soul

(Tune: traditional - spiritual)

Rock my soul in the bosom of Abraham,
Rock my soul in the bosom of Abraham,
Rock my soul in the bosom of Abraham,
O rock-a-my soul.

So high I can't get over it,
So low I can't get under it,
So wide I can't get round of it,
O rock-a-my soul.

A little talk

(Tune: traditional)

A little talk with Jesus makes it right, all right,
A little talk with Jesus makes it right, all right,
In trials of every kind, praise God, I always find
A little talk with Jesus makes it right, all right.

Count your blessings

Count your blessings, name them one by one
Count your blessings, see what God has done,
Count your blessings, name them one by one,
And it will surprise you what the Lord has done.

H-A-P-P-Y
(Tune: traditional)

I'm H-A-P-P-Y, I'm H-A-P-P-Y,
I know I am, I'm sure I am,
I'm H-A-P-P-Y.

My God is so big
(Tune: traditional)

My God is so big,
So strong and so mighty,
There's nothing that he cannot do.

My God is so big,
So strong and so mighty,
There's nothing that he cannot do.

The mountains are his,
The valleys are his,
The stars are his handiwork too,
My God is so big,
So strong and so mighty,
There's nothing that he cannot do.

Creepy crawlies
(Tune – Twinkle, twinkle, little star)

Woodlice crawl and beetles run,
Spiders hide when webs are spun,
Worms they wriggle, moths they fly,
None can walk like you and I.

Stop, look, think
(Tune – Three blind mice)

Stop – look – think,
Stop – look – think,
Before you cross the street,
Before you cross the street,
You use your eyes and you use your ears,
You use your eyes and you use your ears,
And if no cart or car appears,
Why then you cross the street.

Wash your dirty knees

(Tune – A hunting we will go)

Oh wash your dirty knees,
Wash your dirty knees,
Polish your face,
Don't be a disgrace,
And wash your dirty knees.

Oh wash your dirty knees,
Wash your dirty knees,
Scrub each hand,
Do you understand,
And wash your dirty knees.

Oh wash your dirty knees,
Wash your dirty knees,
Clean each ear
And then you will hear
Oh wash your dirty knees.

Oh wash your dirty knees,
Wash your dirty knees,
With a rub-a-dub-dub,
And a jolly good scrub,
You've washed your dirty knees,

The worm

(Tune – There's a long trail)

There's a long, long worm a crawling
Across the flap of my tent,
I can hear the bugle calling,
And it's time that I went,
There's some icy water waiting
For me to take my morning dip,
And when I return, I find that worm
Is on my pillowslip.

That worm it went on crawling
Throughout the heat of the day,
Round and round my tentpole,
And it would not go away,
Oh! It really was a nuisance,
Because it spoilt my evening wash,
And when I laid me down to rest
That worm it went squish – squash!

Ten Bluebottles
(Tune: Ten Green Bottles)

Ten Bluebottles sitting on the meat,
Ten Bluebottles sitting on the meat,
And if one Bluebottle
Should wipe its dirty feet
Then somebody's dinner
Would not be fit to eat.

Nine Bluebottles etc

London's burning
(4 parts)

London's burning, London's burning
Look yonder! Look yonder!
Fire, fire! Fire,fire!
Pour on water, pour on water.

Kids' Songtime!

What shall we do with the drunken sailor

What shall we do with the drunken sailor
What shall we do with the drunken sailor
What shall we do with the drunken sailor
Early in the morning?

(Chorus)   *Hooray and up she rises*
               Hooray and up she rises
               Hooray and up she rises
               Early in the morning

Put him in the long-boat 'til he's sober.

Chorus

Pull out the plug and wet him all over.

Chorus

Put him in the scuppers with a hose-pipe on him.

Chorus

Heave him by the leg in a running bowline.

Chorus

Tie him on the taffrail when she's yard-arm under.

Chorus

That's what we'll do with the drunken sailor.

Chorus

When I first came to this land

(Tune: traditional)

When I first came to this land,
I was not a wealthy man,
So I got myself a shack,
And I did what I could.
And I called my shack, break my back.
But the land was sweet and good,
And I did what I could.

When I first came to this land,
I was not a wealthy man.
So I got myself a cow,
And I did what I could.
And I called my cow, no milk now,
And I called my shack, break my back.
But the land was sweet and good,
And I did what I could.

When I first came to this land,
I was not a wealthy man.
So I got myself a cow,
And I did what I could.
And I called my wife, run for your life,
And I called my cow, no milk now,
And I called my shack, break my back.
But the land was sweet and good,
And I did what I could.

So I got myself a hen
And I called my hen, now and then.

So I got myself a donkey
And I called my donkey, horse gone wonky.

So I got myself a son
And I called my son, my work's done.

There's a hole in my bucket
(Tune: traditional)

There's a hole in my bucket, dear Liza, dear Liza.
There's a hole in my bucket, dear Liza a hole.

Then mend it dear Henry, dear Henry, dear Henry.
Then mend it dear Henry, dear Henry mend it!

With what shall I mend it, dear Liza, dear Liza?
With what shall I mend it, dear Liza with what?

With straw dear Henry, dear Henry, dear Henry.
With straw dear Henry, dear Henry with straw.

But the straw is too long, dear Liza, dear Liza.
The straw is too long, dear Liza too long.

Then cut it dear Henry, dear Henry, dear Henry.
Then cut it dear Henry, dear Henry cut it.

continued...

With what shall I cut it, dear Liza, dear Liza?
With what shall I cut it, dear Liza with what?

Try a knife dear Henry, dear Henry, dear Henry.
Try a knife dear Henry, dear Henry a knife.

But the knife is too blunt, dear Liza, dear Liza.
The knife is too blunt, dear Liza too blunt.

Then sharpen it dear Henry, dear Henry, dear Henry
Then sharpen it dear Henry, dear Henry sharpen it!

With what shall I sharpen it, dear Liza, dear Liza.
With what shall I sharpen it, dear Liza, with what?

Try a stone dear Henry, dear Henry, dear Henry
Try a stone dear Henry, dear Henry try a stone!

But the stone seems too dry, dear Liza, dear Liza.
But the stone seems too dry, dear Liza, too dry.

Then wet it dear Henry, dear Henry, dear Henry
Then wet it dear Henry, dear Henry wet it.

With what shall I wet it, dear Liza, dear Liza?
With what shall I wet it, dear Liza with what?

Try water dear Henry, dear Henry, dear Henry
Try water dear Henry, dear Henry try water!

In what shall I fetch it, dear Liza, dear Liza?
In what shall I fetch it, dear Liza in what?

In a bucket dear Henry, dear Henry, dear Henry
In a bucket dear Henry, dear Henry a bucket

But there's a hole in my bucket, dear Liza, dear Liza.
There's a hole in my bucket, dear Liza a hole.

Row, row
(Tune: traditional)

Row, row, row your boat,
Gently down the stream,
Merrily, merrily, merrily, merrily,
Life is but a dream.

Row, row, row your boat,
Gently down the stream,
If you see a crocodile,
don't forget to scream!

Row, row, row your boat,
Gently down the stream,
If you see an elephant
give him your ice cream!

Soap, soap, soap and towel,
Towel and water please,
Merrily, merrily, merrily, merrily,
Scrub your dirty knees.

Magic penny
(Tune: traditional)

Love is something if you give it away, give it away,
Give it away.
Love is something if you give it away,
You end up having more,
So it's just like a magic penny.
Hold it tight and you won't have any,
Lend it, spend it and you'll have so many,
They'll roll all over the floor, For;
Love is something if you give it away, give it away, give
   it away
Love is something if you give it away, you end up
   having more.

Food terrible food
(Tune: Food, glorious food!)

Food terrible food, burnt sausage and mustard.
We're not in the mood, for cold porridge and custard.
Fried eggs with their edges black,
What next is the question?
We're all gonna suffer from in-di-gestion.
Food terrible food, those soggy old cornflakes,
That lumpy fruit duff, that's all that our cook makes.
We have to eat the stuff, don't want to be rude,
But food – horrible food – sickening food – terrible food.